Egyptian things to make and do

Emily Bone

Designed and illustrated by
Josephine Thompson

Additional design and illustrations by Samantha Chandler,
Antonia Miller, Non Figg and Abigail Brown

Steps and stickers illustrated by Molly Sage

Photographs by Howard Allman

Contents

Scarab beetle

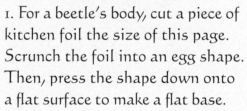

1. For a beetle's body, cut a piece of kitchen foil the size of this page. Scrunch the foil into an egg shape. Then, press the shape down onto a flat surface to make a flat base.

2. Lay the body on a piece of cardboard and draw around it. Cut out the shape. Then, spread white glue on the cardboard and press the body onto it.

3. Rip up lots of pieces of bright tissue paper. Then, lay the beetle on some plastic foodwrap. Brush part of the beetle's body with white glue.

4. Press the pieces of tissue paper onto the wet glue. Then, brush more glue onto the body and press on more tissue paper until the beetle is completely covered.

Scarab beetles are dung beetles that live in Egypt. The Ancient Egyptians thought that the beetles brought good luck. They often gave each other statues in the shape of scarab beetles as good luck charms.

You could draw different patterns on the beetle's wings.

5. Fold a piece of thick paper in half. Then, draw three legs on the paper, like this. Keeping the paper folded, cut out the shapes to make six legs.

6. Tape the legs onto the bottom of the beetle. Then, fold another piece of paper in half and draw a beetle's wing. Cut out the shape through both layers of paper.

7. Draw around the wings with a gold pen and add some lines. Glue them onto the body. Cut circles for eyes and draw on dots. Then, glue them onto the beetle.

Dancers paperchain

The arm that bends up should be pointing the way the man is facing.

1. Cut a long rectangle of paper and fold it in half so that the short ends are together. Then, fold the paper in half again, to make four layers of paper.

2. Draw a triangle for a man's body. Then, draw an upside-down triangle overlapping the first. Add a circle for a head. Then, erase where the triangles overlap.

3. Draw a nose and chin on one side of the head, and hair on the other side. Add two arms, one bending up and one bending down, so the hands touch the edges.

Use the ideas on these pages to draw different outfits for your dancers.

Dancing was very popular in Ancient Egypt. Groups of dancers often performed complicated routines to entertain guests at parties.

For longer hair, draw a straight line from the circle to the shoulder in step 3.

Don't cut along the folds marked in red.

4. Add two legs facing the same way so that the feet touch the edges. Then, holding the layers together, cut out the shape. Don't cut the folds by the hands and feet.

5. Unfold the paper. Draw the eyes and skirt, then fill in around them using a brown felt-tip pen. Use a black pen to draw the eyes, eyebrows and hair.

Other ideas

Draw this shape for a dancing lady paperchain like the one at the top of this page.

Draw one arm along the fold for people dancing back-to-back.

Nefertiti collage

This collage was decorated using paperclips, beads, corrugated cardboard and kitchen sponge cloth - but you can use any materials you want for your collage.

Nefertiti was an Egyptian queen. Egyptians thought that she was very beautiful because of her long, slender neck. This collage is of a famous statue made by Ancient Egyptian artists.

1. Draw a head turned to one side on brown paper. Add a long, thin neck. Then, cut out the head and neck, and glue the shape onto a big piece of paper.

2. Cut a large triangle from red paper for Nefertiti's body. Then, cut a curved piece from the top corner. Glue it at the bottom of the paper, overlapping the neck.

3. Cut a curved strip of blue paper and glue it onto the body. Then, decorate the body with things such as sequins, beads, paperclips and scrunched-up foil balls.

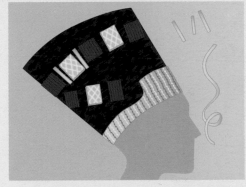

4. Cut a tall shape with curved ends from material for a crown. Glue it onto the head. Then, draw a shape for the bottom of the crown on a piece of cardboard.

5. Cut out the cardboard shape and glue it onto the crown, overlapping the head. Then, cut out eight small squares from red paper and blue material.

6. Glue a row of squares near the top of the crown, and another row halfway across it. Cut short lengths of ribbon and glue them between the squares.

7. Glue a button onto the face for an eye. Then, brush white glue in an oval around the button and add a line coming out, like this. Press black yarn onto the glue.

8. Cut a short piece from a pipe cleaner or yarn and bend it into a curve. Glue it above the eye for an eyebrow. Then, draw a small heart on pink paper for lips.

9. Cut out the heart and glue it sideways onto the face. Then, cut a small oval from brown paper for an ear and glue it on, so that it overlaps the crown.

Nile picture

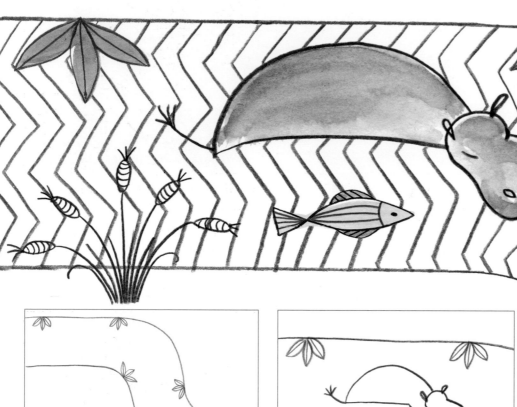

1. Using a blue pencil, draw a wide curving river across a piece of white paper. Then, draw plants with three leaves along the edges of the river.

2. Draw an arch for a hippo's back with a black pencil. Add a head, ears and a tail. Then, draw a blue line from the tail to the head, like this.

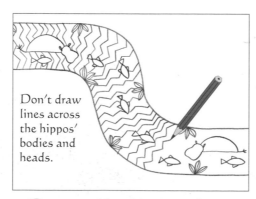

Don't draw lines across the hippos' bodies and heads.

3. For a fish swimming in the river, draw an oval for the body and add a tail. Then, draw a triangle for fins above and below the fish's body.

4. Draw another hippo and some more fish in the river. Then, use a blue pencil to draw lots of zigzag lines across the river for water, like this.

Use brown, blue and black pencils to draw flowers and rushes along the river.

An ibis is a bird that still lives by the River Nile.

5. Use a black pencil to draw the body of an ibis next to the river. Then, draw a circle for the head a little way away from the body, and add a long neck.

6. Draw a long, curved beak. Then, draw a wing on either side of the body, and add feathers along the bottom of each wing. Add two long legs, feet and a tail.

7. Fill in the hippos and plants using watery blue paint. Then, paint the fish yellow with blue fins. Use brown paint for the head, neck and body of the ibis.

You could draw another ibis on the other side of the river.

The Nile is a river that runs through Egypt. In Ancient Egypt, people transported gold and spices in boats on the river. Hippos in the river sometimes attacked the boats, so people gave gifts to the hippo goddess Tauret. They hoped this would stop the hippos from attacking them.

8. When the paint is dry, draw faces on the hippos. Add eyes to the ibis and fish. Then, use a red pencil to draw lines on the fish, like this.

Pharaoh's headdress

1. For the headband, cut a strip of paper that fits around your head. Tape the ends together. Then, cut another strip to go under your chin and tape it onto the headband.

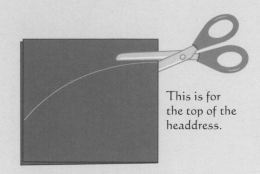

This is for the top of the headdress.

2. Cut a thick strip of paper that is a little wider than your face. Fold it in half and draw a curved line across the paper to the fold. Cut along the line, through both layers.

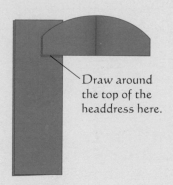

Draw around the top of the headdress here.

3. For the sides, cut a long strip of paper and fold it in half. Then, unfold the top of the headdress. Lay one corner on the folded paper and draw around it.

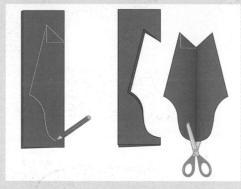

4. Draw a line across the corner to make a triangle. Then, draw the side of the headdress along the fold. Cut out the shape and unfold it. Then, cut along the fold.

5. Cut about 20 thin strips of gold paper for the stripes on the headdress. Glue them onto the top and across both sides, about a finger's width apart.

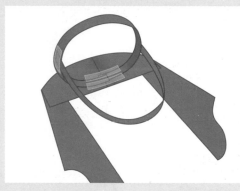

6. Trim off the ends of the strips. Then, glue the two sides onto the top of the headdress. Tape the headband from step 1 onto the back of the headdress, like this.

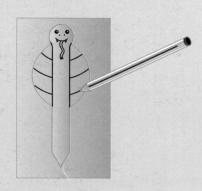

7. Draw a snake with a long body on gold paper. Add a hood below the head. Use a black ballpoint pen to draw a face and lines on the hood. Cut out the snake.

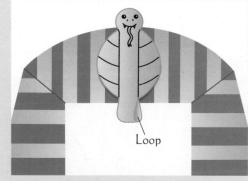

Loop

8. Fold the end of the snake's tail behind its body. Then, tape it onto the snake's back, leaving a loop. Glue the snake onto the top of the headdress.

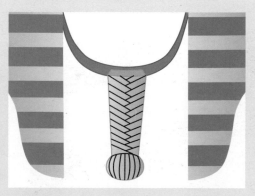

9. Draw a long beard on gold paper. Add a pattern using the black pen, then cut out the shape. Fold over the top of the beard, then glue it onto the chin strap.

To wear the headdress, put the headband over your head and slide the chin strap under your chin.

Egyptian kings were called pharaohs. Pharaohs wore crowns that were covered with a striped blue and gold headdress. A statue of the snake goddess, Wadjet, was attached to the front of the headdress.

Mummy

1. For a mummy's head, scrunch up a piece of kitchen foil into a small, tight ball. Then, scrunch up a larger piece of foil into a sausage shape for a body.

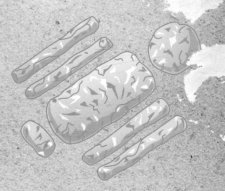

2. Scrunch up four thin sausage shapes about the length of the body for arms and legs. Then, roll a small foil shape for the mummy's feet.

Press the foil around the body parts as you wrap.

3. Arrange the parts of the mummy in the middle of a large piece of kitchen foil, like this. Then, carefully wrap the foil around them to hold them together.

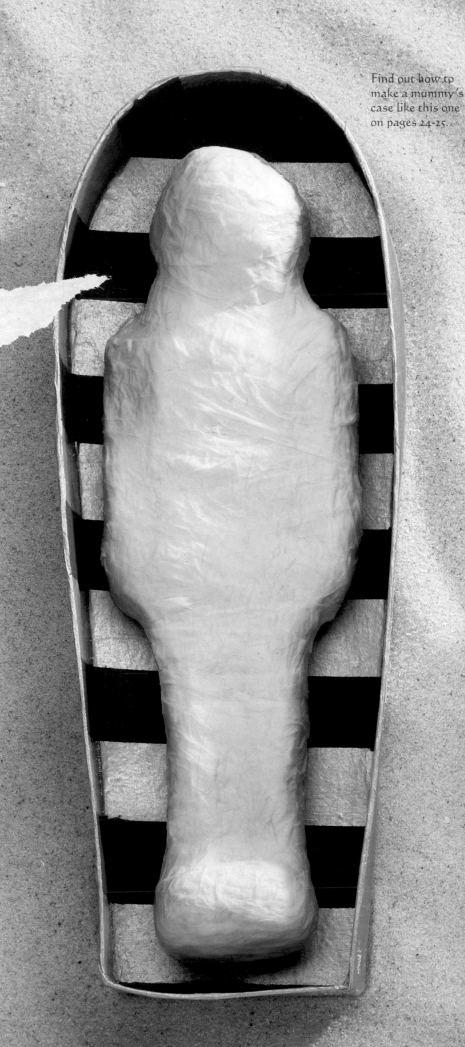

Find out how to make a mummy's case like this one on pages 24-25.

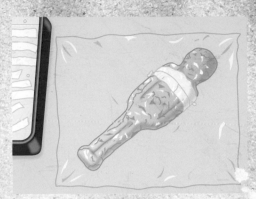

4. Rip some paper towels into about 20 strips that are about the width of your finger. Soak the strips in a small dish of water until they are completely wet.

5. Lay the mummy on plastic foodwrap. Then, take a strip of paper towel out of the water and wrap it around the body and arms like a bandage.

6. Wrap another strip around the mummy. Continue to wrap overlapping strips around the mummy until the foil is completely covered.

You could also make a mummy in the shape of an animal, such as a cat.

7. When the mummy is dry, brush white glue all over the bandages to secure them. Then, leave the mummy on the plastic foodwrap until the glue is dry.

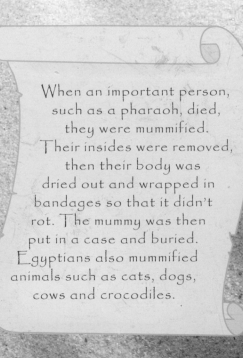

When an important person, such as a pharaoh, died, they were mummified. Their insides were removed, then their body was dried out and wrapped in bandages so that it didn't rot. The mummy was then put in a case and buried. Egyptians also mummified animals such as cats, dogs, cows and crocodiles.

Stand-up camels

Draw the camel's back along the fold.

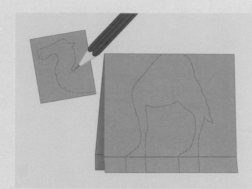

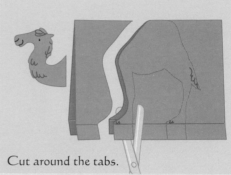

Cut around the tabs.

1. Fold a rectangle of thick paper in half. Fold up the bottom edges of the paper to make flaps, then unfold them. Draw a camel's body, legs and tail above the flaps.

2. Add lines coming down from the legs to the bottom of the flaps to make tabs. Then, draw a camel's head and long neck on another piece of paper.

3. Draw a face using a thin black pen and add brown lines for fur. Cut out the head. Then, keeping the paper folded, cut out the body. Don't cut along the camel's back.

You could make more camels with different saddles and add strips of fabric for bridles.

For thousands of years, people have used camels to carry them on long journeys across the Egyptian desert. This is because after drinking lots of water, a camel can go for days without drinking anything else.

For a palm tree draw a trunk and add tabs at the bottom. Then, glue leaves onto the top of the trunk.

4. Spread glue onto the front of the camel's neck. Slide the neck between the layers at the front of the camel's body. Then, press the neck onto the body.

5. For the base, fold the tabs under the body. Then, glue one tab on top of the other, like this. Press the tabs together until the glue sticks.

6. Cut out a rectangle of material, as wide as the camel's back. Glue it on. Then, cut out smaller rectangles from different material and glue them on to make a saddle.

Egyptian cuff

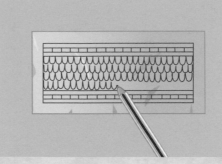

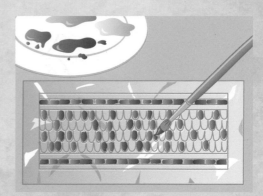

1. For a cuff, cut a wide rectangle from cardboard that fits around your wrist. Then, lay the cuff on the non-shiny side of a piece of kitchen foil and draw around it.

2. Cut around the foil rectangle, leaving a border. Use a ballpoint pen to draw lines across the top and bottom of the rectangle. Then, draw rows of feathers in between.

3. Turn the foil over. Squeeze blobs of glue onto an old plate. Then, mix different food dyes or inks into each blob. Use a brush to fill in the patterns.

Use the ideas on this page to decorate your cuff with different patterns.

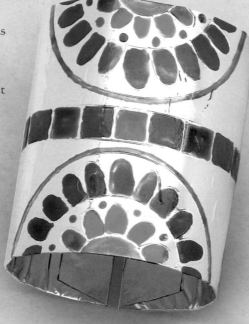

Egyptians wore cuffs around their wrists. The cuffs were made from gold and decorated with precious jewels.

4. When the glue has dried, turn the foil over. Brush glue over the back. Then, press the cardboard rectangle from step 1 onto the middle of the foil. Fold over the edges of the foil.

To make a gold bracelet like the one below, use the foil wrapper from a big chocolate bar.

Leaving the glue to dry will help the cuff to keep its shape.

5. Bend the cuff around until the ends meet. Tape the ends together along the inside of the cuff. Leave the cuff for an hour until the glue dries. Then, cut along the tape.

Painted beetles

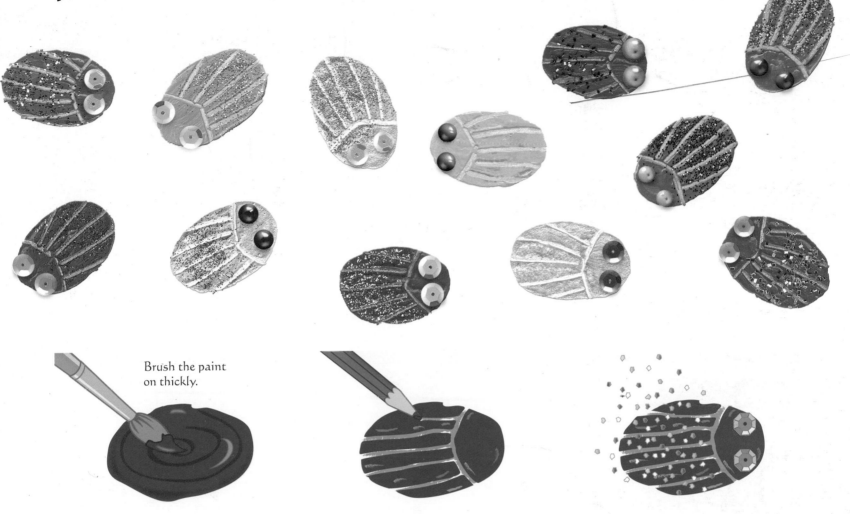

Brush the paint on thickly.

1. Pour some paint onto an old plate, then mix in a little white glue. Dip a paintbrush into the mixture and paint an oval for a beetle on a piece of paper.

2. While the paint is still wet, use a blunt pencil to scrape a curved line across the beetle for a head. Then, scrape lines along its back, like this, for a shell.

3. Press two sequins for eyes onto the beetle's head. Before the glue dries, sprinkle a little glitter over the beetle's back. Then, shake off any excess glitter.

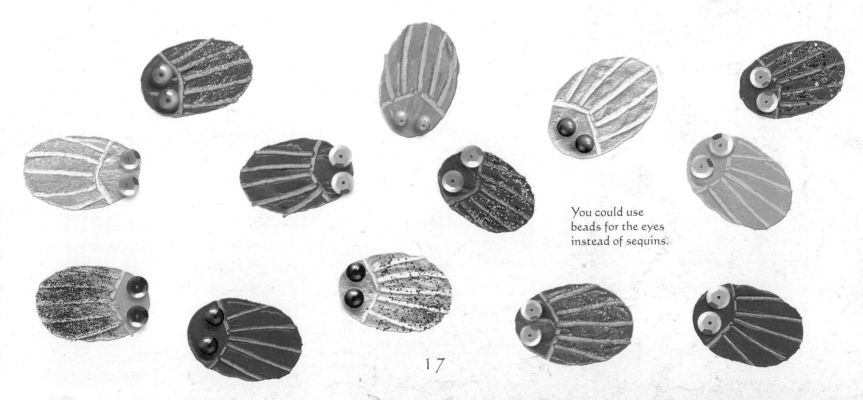

You could use beads for the eyes instead of sequins.

Falcon necklace

If you don't have a paper plate, you could cut a big circle from thin cardboard.

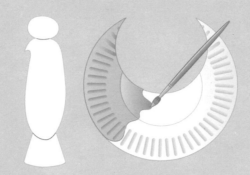

The strip should be a little wider than the falcon's body.

1. To make a falcon's wings, lay a big roll of sticky tape on a paper plate so that the tape touches the edge of the plate. Draw around the roll of tape, then cut out the circle.

2. Draw a falcon's body and tail on a piece of thin cardboard. Add an oval on top of the head, then cut out the shape. Brush gold paint over the falcon's wings and body.

3. Draw a line on some shiny paper and add feathers below it. Cut them out, then brush glue along the top of the strip. Glue it near the bottom of the body.

Glue the feathers so that they overlap the first strip slightly.

4. Draw strips of feathers on different papers, then cut them out. Brush glue across the top of a strip. Then, glue the feathers onto the body above the first strip.

5. Glue the strips up the body until you reach the head. Then, cut around the body. Cut an oval from red paper and glue it on top of the head. Draw a face and beak.

6. Cut a piece of shiny paper as long as a drinking straw. Spread glue on the back of the paper and lay a straw along the edge. Tightly roll the paper around the straw.

Leave space at the ends of the string so you can tie the pectoral around your neck.

7. Cover ten more straws with different papers. Cut pieces the same length as the tail from two of the straws, then glue them on, like this.

8. Glue the body onto the wings. Cut the other straws into smaller pieces. Then, glue some of the pieces in two curved lines along the falcon's wings.

9. Tape a piece of string to the back of each wing. Then, thread the remaining pieces of straw onto the string, like this. Tie a big knot in each end to secure the straws.

A pectoral was a necklace with a large ornament on it. The necklace on this page is a pectoral of the sun god, Ra. Pectorals like this were made from gold and expensive jewels. Only an important person, such as a pharaoh, would have worn it.

Pyramids at sunset

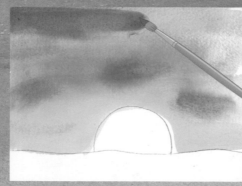

1. Pressing lightly with a pencil, draw a line near the bottom of a piece of paper. Add a half-circle for a sun. Then, paint watery yellow paint on the sky, around the sun.

2. Without cleaning your brush, paint patches of watery orange paint over the yellow paint. Then, paint a strip of pink paint across the top of the picture, like this.

3. When the paint is dry, erase the pencil lines for the sun. Draw a triangle for a pyramid overlapping the sun. Then, add two smaller pyramids on either side.

4. Draw a camel's body with a humped back a little way away from the pyramids. Add a head and long neck. Then, draw four legs that go down to the line.

5. Draw another camel next to the first one. Then, use black paint to fill in the area below the line. Fill in the pyramids and camels, too.

6. Use a thin black pen to add ears, a tail and reins to each camel. Draw a man on one camel's back and luggage on the other. Then, add a man in front of the camels.

You could use a thin black pen to draw palm trees, like these.

Canopic jars

Find out how to draw
hieroglyphics on page 32.

1. Cut a rectangle of paper that is as tall as a jar and long enough to wrap around it, with a little overlap. Draw a line where the ends overlap to make a tab.

2. Unroll the paper and draw gold stripes along the top and bottom. Then, cut a strip of paper that is as tall as the rectangle. Draw hieroglyphics down the strip.

3. Glue the strip down the middle of the paper rectangle. Then, spread glue on the tab and wrap the paper around the jar, pressing the ends together until they stick.

You could make more jars with a different god head on each one to keep all kinds of things inside the jars.

Hapy (lungs)

Duamutef (stomach)

Qebehsenuef (intestines)

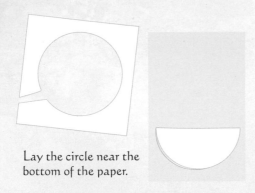

Lay the circle near the bottom of the paper.

4. Take the lid off the jar. Lay it on a piece of paper and draw around it. Cut out the circle, then fold it in half. Lay it on a piece of thick yellow paper, like this.

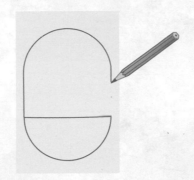

5. Pressing lightly with a pencil, draw around the half-circle. Then, draw a tall arch coming up from the sides of the half-circle you have drawn.

A jackal is a wild dog with pointed ears.

6. Draw a jackal's head and neck on the arch and add pointed ears coming out from the top. Fill in the head using felt-tip pens, and add stripes on either side.

Do not spread glue below the dotted line.

7. Cut out the shape and lay it on another piece of thick yellow paper. Draw around it, and cut out the shape. Then, spread glue on the back of the jackal's head.

8. Press the two shapes together. Fold up the half-circle, like this. Then, turn the shape over and fold up the other side. Open out both sides to make two flaps.

When a person was mummified, their stomach, intestines, lungs and liver were taken out and put in pots called canopic jars. The lids of the jars were made to look like gods. The Egyptians believed that the gods guarded what was in each jar.

9. Open out both the flaps so that they are flat. Screw the lid back onto the jar. Then, spread glue onto the lid and press the flaps onto it.

Mummy case

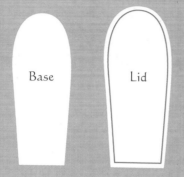

Base   Lid

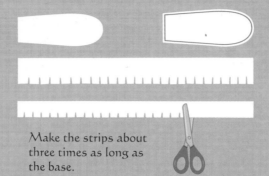

Make the strips about three times as long as the base.

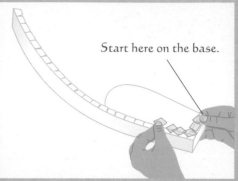

Start here on the base.

1. Draw a shape for the base of a mummy case on thin cardboard. Cut it out and lay it on another piece of cardboard. Draw around it, then cut it out leaving a thin border.

2. Cut a long strip of cardboard for the sides of the base. Then, cut a slightly thinner strip for the lid. Make flaps by cutting slits along one edge of each strip.

3. Fold over all the flaps on both strips. Then, hold the wider strip against the base and fold the flaps over it. Tape the first few flaps onto the base, like this.

Egyptian mummies were kept in cases made to look like a person. The cases were painted, then covered in pictures and hieroglyphic writing. The person painted on each case was a picture of the man or woman inside.

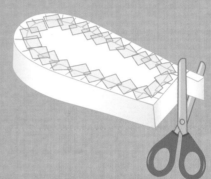

4. Bend the strip all the way around the base, securing the flaps with tape. Trim off any extra cardboard, then tape around the corner where the ends of the strip meet.

The tissue paper makes the lid look 3-D.

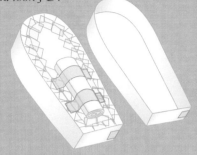

5. Follow steps 3-4 to attach the thinner strip to the lid in the same way. Then, roll some tissue paper into a long shape for legs. Tape it onto the lid, like this.

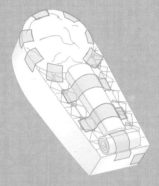

6. Roll some more tissue paper into a ball, then press it down to flatten it. Tape it onto the lid for a head. Then, tape on a small roll of tissue paper for feet.

Find out how to make a mummy to put inside your case on pages 12-13.

Glue tissue paper onto the inside and bottom of the case, too.

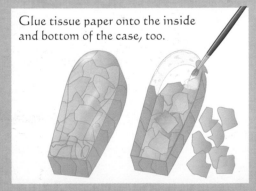

7. Rip up pieces of gold tissue paper. Brush white glue on part of the lid and press on paper. Continue to brush on glue and press on paper until the whole case is covered.

Use a thin paintbrush and black paint if you don't have a pen with permanent ink.

8. When the glue is dry, use a black felt-tip pen with permanent ink to draw a face and beard. Draw a shape for a headdress and fill it in with black paint.

Find out more about hieroglyphics on page 32.

9. Decorate the lid using red and green paint. When the paint is dry, add stripes on the headdress using a gold pen. Then, use the black pen to draw hieroglyphics on the case.

Cracked wax tomb picture

This will be the man's body and skirt.

1. Using a pencil, draw a triangle on a piece of white paper. Then, draw an upside-down triangle overlapping the first one. Erase where the triangles overlap.

2. Draw an oval above the body for a head and add lines for a neck. Then, draw a nose and chin on one side of the head. Add hair on the other side, like this.

3. Draw two legs below the body, and add two feet pointing to one side. Then, draw a slanting line across the middle of the man's body to make a skirt.

For a servant carrying a stick, draw his arm bending across his body.

The cracked wax effect makes the picture look like an old tomb painting.

Fill in the whites of the eye with white wax crayon.

4. Add an arm that bends up in a V-shape coming out from one side of the body, like this. Then, draw a flat hand at the end of the arm.

5. Draw a thin rectangle for a flat tray on top of the hand, then draw two pots on top of it. Add a straight arm on the other side of the man's body.

6. Use a black wax crayon to draw an eye and eyebrow on the face, and fill in the hair. Then, fill in the rest of the picture and background using wax crayons.

Make sure you brush paint into all the creases.

7. Scrunch up the paper into a tight ball. Carefully open the paper out again and flatten it. Then, brush dark blue paint all over the picture, like this.

For a serving girl, draw longer hair and a long dress. Draw lots of patterns on the dress and fill them in with wax crayons.

The walls inside a pyramid were often decorated with paintings of scenes from everyday life. The Egyptians painted people with their heads and feet turned to one side. This picture shows servants carrying food to a banquet.

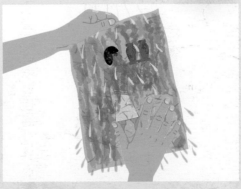

8. Rinse the paper under cold running water. Rub it gently with your hand until you can see the picture again. Then, lay the paper on plastic foodwrap to dry.

Egyptian god puppets

Draw the triangles in the middle of the cardboard.

1. Draw a triangle on a piece of thin cardboard. Then, draw an upside-down triangle overlapping the first one for the body of a god. Erase where the triangles overlap.

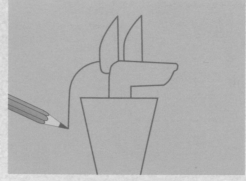

2. Draw a head with a long nose on top of the body. Add two long ears on top of the head. Then, draw hair behind the head and below the chin.

3. Add legs and feet, then draw a rectangle touching the feet. Draw two long sausage shapes for upper arms, near the body. Then, draw the forearms, too.

Fill in the shape between the legs using black paint.

4. Add a face, hair, skirt and anklets using gold, black and white paints. Then, paint cuffs on each wrist. When the paint is dry, cut out the arms and the body.

5. Using a hole puncher, make a hole at the bottom of each upper arm. Punch two holes at the top of the body. Then, cut four strips that fit through the holes.

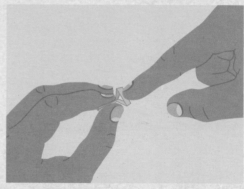

6. Fold a strip into a loop. Hold the strip near the top, then push the top of the loop down to flatten it. Fold the other strips in the same way to make four hinges.

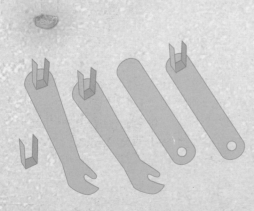

7. Dab white glue onto the flat part of two hinges, and press them onto the back of the forearms, near the top. Glue the other hinges onto the tops of the upper arms.

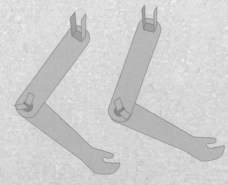

8. Push the ends of a hinge on one forearm through the hole on one upper arm. Fold back the ends of the hinge. Do the same with the other pieces to make another arm.

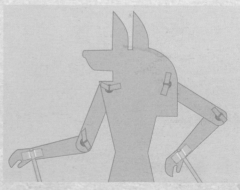

9. Turn the body over and slot the holes on the body onto the hinges at the top of each arm. Fold back the ends. Then, tape a satay or kebab stick onto each wrist.

The Egyptians worshipped over 2,000 gods and goddesses. Many of the gods looked like animals, or people with animal heads. Anubis, who had the head of a jackal, was the god of the dead. People believed he would look after them when they died. Sobek had the head of a crocodile. He was the Egyptian god of water.

Use poster tack to stick the gods to the edge of a table and use the sticks to make the puppets' arms move.

Pyramid gift box

Use a ruler.

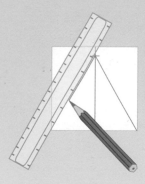

Draw the square in the middle of the paper.

1. Draw an 8cm x 8cm (3in x 3in) square on thin cardboard and cut it out. Make marks 4cm (1½in) along the top and bottom edges, then draw a line down the middle.

2. Make a mark on the line 7cm (2½in) up from the bottom of the cardboard. Then, draw lines from the mark to each bottom corner to make a triangle.

3. Cut out the triangle. Then, draw an 8cm x 8cm (3in x 3in) square on thick paper. Lay the triangle along the top edge of the square and draw around it.

Make bigger pyramids by drawing a bigger square and triangle in step 1.

Wrap a gift in tissue paper and put it inside the pyramid before tying the ribbon.

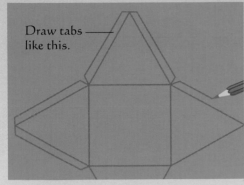

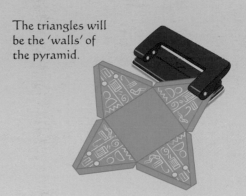

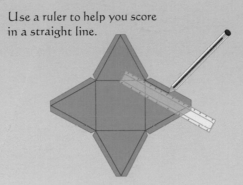

Draw tabs like this.

Use a ruler to help you score in a straight line.

The triangles will be the 'walls' of the pyramid.

4. Lay the triangle along each side of the square and draw around it. Then, draw shapes for tabs along both sides of each triangle, like this.

5. Cut out the shape. Pressing hard with a ballpoint pen, draw along each of the pencil lines to make it easier to fold. This is called scoring.

6. Turn over the shape. Then, use felt-tip pens to decorate the triangles. Punch two holes about a finger's width apart near the top of each triangle.

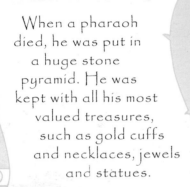

When a pharaoh died, he was put in a huge stone pyramid. He was kept with all his most valued treasures, such as gold cuffs and necklaces, jewels and statues.

7. Turn over the shape. Fold in all the tabs, then fold up all the triangles. Push the end of a ribbon into one hole, then out of the hole in the next triangle.

8. Thread the ribbon in and out of all the holes in the triangles. Then, pull both ends of the ribbon tight and tie the ends together to close the pyramid.

Use the ideas on these pages to draw different pictures on a pyramid. Fill them in using felt-tip pens or paints.

Hieroglyphics

Egyptian writing was made up of painted pictures called hieroglyphs. In Ancient Egypt, each picture stood for a letter, a sound or a whole word. Here are examples of hieroglyphs that you can use to write messages or decorate the things you make.

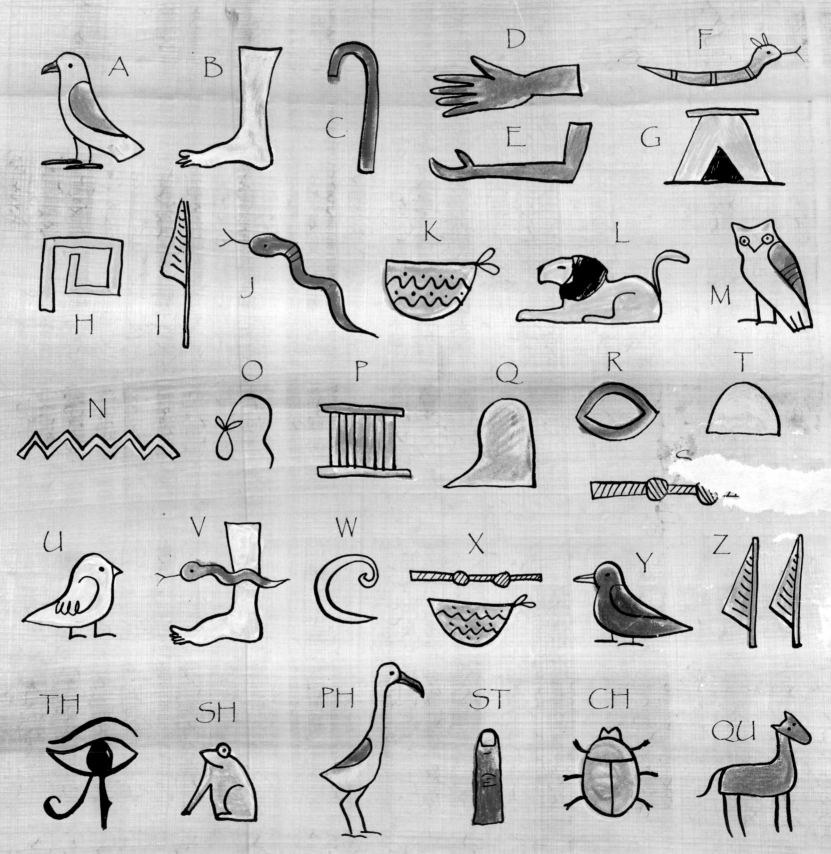

Edited by Leonie Pratt • Series Editor: Fiona Watt • Photographic manipulation by Nick Wakeford
First published in 2009 by Usborne Publishing Ltd., 83-85 Saffron Hill, London, EC1N 8RT, England www.usborne.com